Annie and the Birds

for Annie

Scholastic Children's Books,
Scholastic Publications Ltd,
7-9 Pratt Street, London NW1 0AE, UK

Scholastic Inc.,
730 Broadway, New York, NY 10003, USA

Scholastic Canada Ltd,
123 Newkirk Road, Richmond Hill,
Ontario, Canada L4C 3G5

Ashton Scholastic Pty Ltd,
P O Box 579, Gosford, New South Wales,
Australia

Ashton Scholastic Ltd,
Private Bag 1, Penrose, Auckland,
New Zealand

First published by Scholastic Publications Ltd, 1991
First published in paperback, 1992

Copyright © Kathy Henderson, 1991

ISBN 0 590 55016 0

Printed in Belgium by Proost International Book Production

10 9 8 7 6 5 4 3 2 1

Annie and the Birds

Kathy Henderson

Hippo Books
Scholastic Children's Books
London

Annie went
to the park
to feed
the ducks.

She took some
bread in a big bag

and bit by bit
she threw it
on the ground.

First came
a hopping bobbing
sparrow
and Annie smiled.

Then two
waddly ducks
and Annie laughed.

Then three pigeons
cooing coo coo ricoo
and Annie
flapped her hands.

Then four seagulls
crying like the wind
and Annie
stretched
out
her arms.

Then a big
brown
honking goose
and Annie
ran.

And THEN
came
a sleek
sneaking
hunting
creeping
CAT

and frightened all
the birds into the air.

She wanted
to fly too.
So she ran

Annie was
very sad.

She flapped
her hands,
she laughed
and smiled

and she
stretched out
her arms.

and Annie flew

all the way
home.